MONKY B[US]INESS

Written and illustrated by
Megs Bailey

For my sister Jenny
who shared the halcyon days of my childhood... long summer days
spent on the beach... sandy toes and salty kisses... trips to the
magical Island of Herm... and the occasional riotous nights under
canvas.

Those were special times.
MB

Other titles about Percy:

A Flying Start
Percy's Hat Trick

Published by Tree House Publishing (Guernsey) 2017
Printed by ColourMonster, Guernsey.

ISBN: 978-0-9935275-2-4

A note from the author...

The Guernsey language, known as Guernésiais, is a type of Norman French. As it was a spoken language, different dialects of 'Guernsey Patois' evolved across the island with slight variations in pronunciation and spelling. In fact many of the words were not written down at all!

In my story, you will come across some of the words and phrases I was familiar with when I was growing up. Both my mother and grandmother spoke a little 'patois' but their words sounded slightly different from the same words spoken by my great-aunt who lived in another part of the island.

Some of the spellings and pronunciations in my book may vary from the ones you know. But you'll get the idea of my 'patois' phrases as you put them into the context of the story!

MB

PERCY'S ISLAND HOME

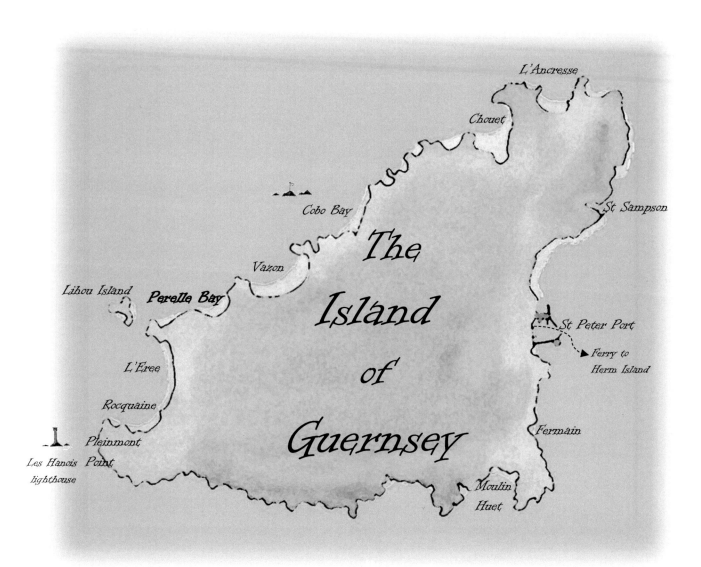

L'Ancresse

Chouet

Cobo Bay

St Sampson

The

Vazon

Island

Lihou Island

Perelle Bay

of

St Peter Port

Ferry to
Herm Island

L'Erée

Guernsey

Rocquaine

Fermain

Pleinmont
Point

Les Hanois
lighthouse

Moulin
Huet

Herm Island

Guernsey, Percy's island home
Is not an island on its own,
The Bailiwick includes some more
Smaller islands found offshore.
Farthest north across the sea
You'll find the Isle of Alderney
Where gannets in enormous flocks
Nest upon the craggy rocks.
Its bays have sand of glistening gold,
And fortresses from days of old.
In the channel, to the east
Not far away, a few miles at least
Lie the Isles of Sark and Brecqhou
Not forgetting Herm and Jethou,
Pretty places, quite unique,
Too small for traffic, so to speak.
On Sark, to get around, of course,
You'll ride a pushang or a horse,
And Herm, if that's the place you choose
You'll need a pair of walking shoes.
When you arrive at Rosaire Landing
Its beauty is just so outstanding
You'll realise you've stepped ashore
A piece of paradise, for sure.

Pushang is a Guernsey word for a bicycle

Dad called the chicks and sat them down
In the nest upon the ground
'The summer's here,' he smiled and said,
'No time to hang about in bed.
The days are long, with hours of sun,
It's time for us to have some fun.
Let me tell you what I did
When I was just like you, a kid.

3

When I was young, your age abouts,
I joined a troop of seagull scouts
We did all sorts of useful things -
Tying knots with ropes and strings.
We learned so many handy tricks,
How to make a fire from sticks,
How to cook, how to row,
How to make a wooden bow
To fire an arrow straight and long,
How to whittle, sing a song,
Send a signal from a lamp,
But, best of all, we learned to camp.
The best days of my youth were spent
Under canvas in a tent.'

As Percy's Dad reminisced
About the camping days he missed
An idea popped into his head.
'I know what we'll do,' he said.

'Come with me, we'll go to Fred's
And look inside his packing sheds.
It's where I store my camping gear
There's not much room to keep it here.
We'll go and see if it's okay
To use again, on holiday.'

Off they went on Dad's new mission
To check and see the tent's condition.
Fred agreed that all was fine,
'I've kept an eye from time to time.
I put it up, just last week
To check for any tear or leak
And even though it rained all night
It looked completely watertight.'

Dad was pleased, he liked old Fred,
He turned and to his mate he said,
'Thank you, Fred, that's kind of you.
Fancy coming camping too?'
'Caw chapin, where are you going?' asked Fred,
'I'm choosy where I rest my head,'
'Herm,' said Dad, 'that's the place for me,
Seagull Campsite – it has to be!'
Yes sireee, the Seagull Site,
That's where we'll spend the next few nights.'

Caw chapin – pronounced
Cor shap-an - means Oh
my goodness!

Fred winked. He said, 'I'd love to! Brill!
I'll go and mention it to Bill.
That tent will be a bit too small
To accommodate us all,
He'll take us over on his boat
We two can spend the nights afloat.'

Percy, Pip and Polly cheered
Excited at what they'd just heard.
'Camping! Whooppee!' Polly cried,
And Percy's eyes, they opened wide.
Pip, jumped up, all agog,
And kept on jumping like a frog.
Dad was going to pitch his tent
Across on Herm! So off they went.

They all flew home on eager wings
To fetch the other camping things
That Mum had started getting ready
While they were seeing Dad's mate, Freddy.

All the food was being packed
Into boxes, neatly stacked.
Carefully Mum checked her list
Ensuring nothing would be missed.
'Sandeels, teabags, bacon, rice
And sausages would be quite nice,
Toasted marshmallows for sweet -
Those would be a tasty treat
Round the campfire after tea,
I'll take an extra bag for me!'

'Now, sleeping bags, a torch, a stove,
We need an awful lot, by jove,
Dishes, spoons, forks and knives,
Glasses, mugs and more besides!'

When Dad came back, he stared a while
At the massive boxy pile.
'We need *all* this stuff? Goodness! Eeek!
We're only going for a week!'

'Of course,' said Mum, 'you'll see we do
You'd be surprised what we get through.
Now, that is everything, I think
Other than the kitchen sink!'

Then with a bit of timely luck
Fred appeared in his old truck
Everything was loaded on
Including each and everyone.
'We're off!' cried Dad. 'To the quay -
We're going camping, you and me!'

As they reached the harbour pier
They first unloaded all their gear
The bustling port was very busy
Enough to make you feel quite dizzy!

Sailing boats and cargo ships,
Passengers on ferry trips
Masts on yachts, and flags and buoys
Most expensive grown-up toys!
And chugging softly alongside
Bill's boat, the *Jenny Wren*, was tied.

The fishing boat, a solid craft
Was neat and tidy, fore and aft
Built in traditional Guernsey style,
Bill had owned her for a while.
Her timber hull was painted white
She was the most delightful sight.

11

The wheelhouse, standing proud, by heck,
Was polished, like the wooden deck.
The ropes were coiled, the brass it gleamed
And Captain Bill waved and beamed.
'Ahoy there, come aboard,' Bill boomed,
'Bring your things, there's lots of room.'
Fred helped Dad to shift the load
And soon their stuff was safely stowed.
The chicks, they started to explore,
And went below to see some more.

They found the galley spick and span
With plates and cups and pots and pans
And in the captain's cabin, slung
Between the beams two hammocks swung.
The chicks looked in to take a peep
To see where Fred and Bill would sleep.

Back on deck, Bill looked about,
Then cast adrift and headed out
Leaving all the harbour bustle
Making for the Little Russell.
Percy perched upon the rail
He almost sat on Polly's tail!
And from the bows here they could see
The spray and waves upon the sea.

The Little Russell is a
stretch of sea between
Guernsey and Herm.
Strong currents often
make it quite rough!

Mum and Dad enjoyed the ride
Sitting on the starboard side,
And as Bill steered, Fred checked the dinghy
(He didn't want to lose the thingy).
Pip, more excited than before,
Just couldn't wait to get ashore.
He flew ahead and circled round,
Then off he went, Hermward bound.

The *Jenny Wren*'s crew soon arrived
At Herm's small harbour. The rising tide
Was pretty high, they disembarked
And, with the tractor ready parked,
Piled their things into the back
Then started walking up the track.
'See you in a while,' called Bill
As they started up the hill,
'We'll moor the boat, and tie it tight
Then meet you at the Seagull Site.'

Before too long the family went
To Seagull field to pitch the tent.
Dad knew what to do, for sure,
He said he'd done this all before.
So he began to tell the others,
Mum and Polly and her brothers,
What to do and where to stand
And how to lend a helping hand.

Setting out each rope and pole
Was quite a lengthy rigmarole
Eventually the tenty bits
Were laid out waiting to be fixed.
'Right', said Dad, 'let's make a start,
Percy, hold these poles apart.

Now Pip, just take this canvas flap
And stretch it over there, good chap.
Polly, grab the other side
And spread it right out, nice and wide.

I'll pull this rope to raise it up
Don't let go till I say 'stop'.
Ready? Go!' Dad pulled it tight
He pulled and pulled with all his might.

The rope swung up, the poles swung round
The tent collapsed and hit the ground!
Percy, Pip and Polly too
Completely disappeared from view,
But underneath the canvas humps
Were three distinctive gull-shaped lumps.

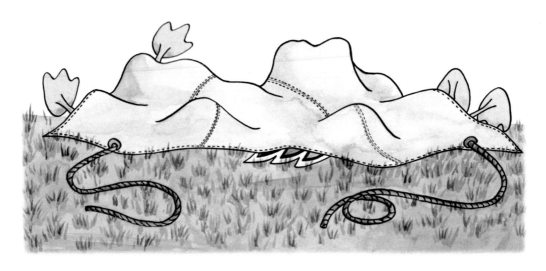

The chicks crawled out from underneath
With bits of grass stuck in their beaks.
And looking quite dishevelled sat
Peering at the tent, all flat.
They tried again, but alas
Same thing happened, the tent collapsed
Again they tried, and then once more…
Each time the tent lay on the floor.

Dad gave up and searched around
Searched for something on the ground
'Now where have those instructions gone?
Have you seen them anyone?
My patience is completely spent
It's ages since I pitched this tent.'
'Mmm,' said Mum, 'it's been a while
And you've forgotten how,' she smiled.
'Yes, I guess you're right,' said Dad,
'My tent erecting skills are bad,
I'm out of practice… been too long…
I think I must have got it wrong,
We'll have to wait for Bill and Fred
They'll have to put it up instead.'

'Warro! Having trouble here?'
Asked Fred, as he and Bill appeared.
'Looks like it's our help you need.'
'Oh yes,' said Dad, 'I do indeed!
Thank goodness - you can lend a wing,
I can't put up the bloney thing!'

Warro is an old Guernsey greeting and bloney is an old Guernsey saying similar to 'blooming'

They all helped Dad to pitch the tent
Within minutes, up it went.
They pulled the guy ropes, pegged them down,
And made sure all was safe and sound.

'Righto,' said Fred, 'we'll see you later
At the Mermaid, say about eight…er…
While you unpack all your dishes
We'll see if we can catch some fishes.

Come on Bill, I've brought my rod
Let's see if we can catch some cod.'
'Brill!' said Dad. 'No…cod,' said Fred,
'Or a mackerel, maybe two,' he said.
'That's not quite what I meant,' said Dad,
'I'm coming too. Brill… I'm glad!'

19

Off they went, no time to waste
Down onto the rocks they raced.
They cast their lines with all their might
And waited for the fish to bite.

At the camp, the chicks helped Mum
And soon the jobs were quickly done.
Food prepared, the table laid,
The sleeping-baggy beds were made.
Mum said, 'Off you go, my chicks,
Go scavenging to find some sticks,
You'll need to find some wood to light
Then build our campfire for tonight.'

When at last the chicks came back,
Mum gave each of them a snack
They'd gathered lots of wood and they
Were feeling peckish, by the way.

But Mum was keen to go exploring
As overhead the sun was soaring
They had to keep out of the heat
And she knew of a cool retreat.

'Hurry up and eat your apple,
We'll go to see St Tugual's chapel
The garden's quite a shady spot
Where we can sit, it's not too hot.'

'It's just around the corner, here,'
Called Mum as they were getting near.
Great excitement filled the air
Some folks were getting married there.

On the garden wall they perched
Peering in the tiny church
To see the couple getting wed,
Listening to the vows they said.

St.Tugual's congregation sang
And afterwards, the bell, it rang.
Then as the couple came outside
The guests all cheered the groom and bride.

They threw confetti in the sky
And rosy petals drifted by.
'It looks like snow,' Pip said with glee
As petals landed on his knee.

'Come on,' said Mum, 'it's getting late
We said we'd meet the men at eight.
The Tavern's just along the track.
We'll have one drink then we'll head back.'

As they reached the Mermaid Inn
Dad waved and signalled to come in
He gave them all a welcome hug,
'We're all inside, here in the snug,
We've caught a lot of fish, eh, Fred?'
I hope you're hungry, kids,' he said.

25

They all sat down and drinks were bought
Dad told them of the fish they'd caught
He listened to his children chat
About the campsite, this and that,
About the sticks they'd found, their bedding,
The fire they'd built, about the wedding.

Dad, Bill and Fred agreed
They'd had a busy day, indeed.
Then, as they sipped their beery ale,
Fred began his ghostly tale.

'Here on Herm, I do believe,
Some centuries ago, there lived
Some monks, indeed, religious men,
And Pierre du Pont was one of them.
Alas, I have to say, my friends,
Pierre came to quite a sticky end.
But over the years folks have said
They've seen his ghost although he's dead.'

'Shh…don't be daft,' Bill gave a wink.
'You'll scare the kids now, don't you think?
There's no such things as ghosts, oh, Fred!
Don't listen to him, kids,' he said.
'It's true,' said Fred, ignoring Bill,
'I didn't believe myself until
My mate, he said he's seen it twice
Seen it with his own two eyes!'

'Honestly, Fred!' Bill banged his fist.
'I'm telling you! Ghosts don't exist!
Your mate…' Bill lowered his voice and spoke
'He's pulling your leg; he's having a joke!'

Fred went on, at a slower pace,
A serious look across his face,
'I believe him, I honestly do
Caw chapin! Would I lie to you?'
Dad knew old Fred told porky pies
And saw the twinkle in his eyes,
Dad flashed a look at Fred. He knew
His story wasn't really true!
Fred looked around and checked the door
And carried on his tale once more.

'Edwin Le Poidevin, my mate, you know,
Well, he stayed here some years ago
At the cottage along the path.
When lighting a fire in the hearth
He heard a noise, a sort of squeak
And heavy footsteps, and a creak
Walking up the stairs.' Fred swallowed.
'So Edwin, feeling brave, he followed.
And right there, on that very landing
A ghostly hooded monk was standing!'

Poidevin is pronounced
Pedvin, and sometimes
spelled that way too.

'So what did Edwin do?' asked Dad.
'It's good you asked me that, I'm glad.
Cor, he couldn't quite believe his eyes
It's fair to say he was surprised!
He blinked – the monk just disappeared
Just…vanished. It was really weird!'

Bill shook and shivered, wheezed and winced
He didn't look at all convinced.
'I don't like this, so stop it, Fred,
You're spooking me too much,' he said.
But Fred continued with his tale
And Bill continued to grow pale.

'The second time he saw the monk
Was when he cleared the Major's junk
At the Manor House one day
When the family went away.
In the basement Edwin saw
A beam of light behind a door
He naturally investigated
Turned the latch and then he waited…
In the room he saw a figure
In a cloak but only bigger
This cloak, it had a hood all right
And gave poor Edwin quite a fright!

'It's you', said Edwin, feeling brave
The monk just raised his hand to wave
And disappeared through the floor
(You'd think that he'd have used the door!)'

Bill, whose face was somewhat whitened
Was nervous, looking very frightened,
He said, 'Kids, don't listen to Fred
Don't go believing what he said.
It's just his silly, made-up yarn
A joke, not meaning any harm.'

Mum quickly gathered up the chicks,
'Right, let's go and get back quick,
Dad, you stay longer if you wish
While we go back and cook the fish.
We'll see you later, in an hour.'
'Okay,' said Dad, 'see you, Flower.'

Pip, quietly walking, deep in thought
Said, 'Do you know what we ought
To do? We should try to pay back Fred
And play a joke on him instead.
I've got a good idea, a plan
We'll trick old Freddy if we can.'

Pip whispered his idea to Polly
Then to Percy, who said, 'Golly,
That's just brilliant! Well done Pip!
We'll need to get Mum's help with this.'

Quickly back to camp they flew
Mum agreed, knew what to do.
She dived into the tent unheeded
Then reappeared with what they needed

29

She'd fetched some stuff - bits of string
Some safety pins and rope and things.
'Now, Polly, sit on Percy's shoulder
And Pip you sit on Polly's…hold her
Very tight and don't let go
Now all stand still and wait a mo…'

Mum took a blanket from her bed
And draped it right across Pip's head
She pinned it here and there to hide
The wobbling tower of gulls inside.
She wrapped the rope around their middle
Hitched it up and with a giggle
Tied two spoons with bits of string
To make a silver pendant thing.

Mum stood back, admired her work
'Perfect,' she said with a wicked smirk.
'Now off you go, but keep your head
We only want to scare old Fred
Keep out of sight from other folk
Remember this is just a joke!'

Looking like an old monk should
Dressed in a habit complete with hood,
A rope with knots tied round the waist
And a cross hanging down on a leathery lace,
The chicks crossed the field along the edge
Deep in the shadows of the brambly hedge.

They made their way back down the hill
Keeping out of sight until
They hid behind a leafy shrub
By the entrance to the Mermaid Pub.

They didn't have to wait too long
Until they heard Fred's usual song
Getting nearer, closer, till
Like a statue, the chicks kept still.
Fred and Bill stood in the light
Dad stopped them both to say, 'Goodnight'.

As they heard their familiar voices
Pip started making ghostly noises,
'*Whooo…*,' he moaned and, '*Whooo…*,' again
Really spooking all the men.

'*Whoooooooo-ooou-ooooo…….* '
Pip wailed a soft and ghostly sound
Fred and Bill and Dad turned round.
'What was that?' Bill grabbed Dad's wing
I heard a noise, what was that thing? '

'Who's there? ' said Fred, 'Quiet…shush,
The noise is coming from that bush!'
'*Whooooooo…….* ' Pip wailed louder still
As they slowly moved in front of Bill.

The monky apparition stood
And Pip pulled down the blanket hood
To hide his beak, just in case
The others recognized his face.
Below him Polly sneezed and wriggled
And Percy grabbed her feet and giggled.

'*WHOOOOOOO.........*'
Pip wailed louder to hide their laughter
Trying to avert disaster
The more they chuckled the more Pip howled!
'I'm Pierre Le Pont. *Whoooooo...,*' he growled.

Fred, eyes wide open, he just stared
As the ghostly monk loomed there.
He gulped. He blinked and blinked again
Then turned and scampered down the lane!

'Arrgghh... It's him…the g..g..ghost!' yelled Fred,
'I'm off, back to the boat,' he said.
'We're out of here,' Bill turned to Dad
'I'm not staying here, too bad -
This place is haunted, Fred was right
We're going to go back home tonight!

We'll come and fetch you in a week.'
He turned and opened wide his beak,
'Wait for me,' yelled Bill, 'Hey Fred,
Wait! I'm coming too,' he said.
'Don't leave me here, I'm scared of ghosts
And this one's scarier than most!'

By now the chicks, in fits of laughter
Watched as Bill, in fear, chased after
Fred who'd disappeared from sight.
Terrified, he'd taken flight.

Dad looked closely, double checked,
Suspiciously he gently pecked
And pulled the blanket just a bit
To see what was inside of it.

'Now… just a minute, I don't think
That ghostly monks are dressed in… pink!'
He grabbed the blanket, they were rumbled
Suddenly the chicks all tumbled
And on the pathway Dad could see
Sprawled out, his children, one, two, three.

'You little monkeys!' he declared,
'You've frightened Fred and Bill is scared.
I must admit you look the part
At first you gave me quite a start!'
'It serves Fred right, Dad,' Percy said.
'We played him at his game instead.'
'You did,' said Dad, 'Fred's had a shock
Let's hope his storytelling stops.
Come along, you three, that's quite
Enough excitement for one night.'

They made their way back to the tent
Told Mum about the whole event
They laughed as they recalled Fred's fright
And how Bill's face had turned so white!
Mum grinned and said, 'My clever chicks,
That might stop Fred from playing his tricks.
Pip's idea to play this prank,
Was great - it's him we need to thank.'

The fire was lit, the fish were cooked
Across the fields the campers looked.
They could see the lights on Sark
Flickering, twinkling in the dark.

'Time for bed now,' Dad said, yawning,
'We'll see you monkeys in the morning.
Nighty, night and all sleep tight,
Don't you let the bibeets bite!'

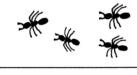

Bibeets are creepy crawlies

Every day was sunny and
They had such fun upon the sand...
The boys dug pools, built castles high
With turrets reaching to the sky.
Polly liked collecting shells, each
Kind was waiting on the beach
And she'd spend hours finding more
Pretty treasures on the shore.
Shell Beach was her favourite spot
That's where she'd always find a lot.

Sometimes they'd swoop and soar and skim
And fly to Belvoir Bay to swim
Then round the south coast cliffs they'd glide
And sometimes, when they all grew tired
When their wings were sore and stiff
They'd stop and sit up on the cliff
By the grassy, burrow nests
With the puffins, there they'd rest.

Then off to Jethou in the sun
Fly there and back - just for fun
The oystercatchers called their names
And joined in all their seagull games.

And with their nights spent in the tent
Incredibly the time just went
The week flew by (excuse the pun!)
Enjoyed, of course by everyone.

All good things end, I have to mention,
And camping trips are no exception,
Soon their tent and stuff were packed
And ready to be taken back
By tractor down the hill and then
To Rosaire and the *Jenny Wren.*
The low tide meant that Bill and Fred
Had to tie up there instead.

They said they didn't go ashore
In case they saw the ghost once more.
'Oh, really, Fred, you've both been tricked,'
Dad laughed, pointing to his chicks.
'There really are no ghosts, you see,
That monk you saw was just these three.'
When Dad explained the joke they laughed,
(Although they both felt really daft)!

Fred chuckled, turned to Dad, and sighed,
'We've been taken for a ride
You mean it was these children, eh?
You had us there, kids, I must say!
But change my ways? Not a jot!
No leopards or Guernseymen change their spots!'

As the *Jenny Wren* left Rosaire's shore
Dad turned to gaze at Herm once more
They'd all had such a great time here
He vowed that they'd return next year.
The ghost, the trick, had all been fun
With days of sea and sand and sun.

Herm was in the distance now
But Dad could just make out somehow...
He blinked and he began to stare
Beneath the arch, was someone there?
In the shadows a tall man stood
Did he wear a cloak and hood?
Dad looked again. The sun was bright
It could have been a trick of light...
But from the corner of his eye
Dad saw the figure wave goodbye.

About the author...

Megs Bailey was born on her beloved Island of Guernsey and enjoyed a wonderful childhood exploring the beautiful beaches and other bailiwick islands.

'Monky Business' is the third story set in the islands Megs loves, where she lives with her husband, Jeff, and a houseful of gulls.

Ironman Haw

My Story

A Ten Year Dream. A Two Year Plan

Frank Adornato

Why am I writing this book?

04 October 2014,

I raced my first Ironman Triathlon in Kona Hawaii on October 15th, 1994. 2.4 miles swimming / 112 miles cycling / 26.2 miles running. That race ranks as one of my greatest personal accomplishments. Its been twenty years since that first Ironman race, and as I sit here writing this, athletes are arriving in Kona for another Ironman Triathlon World Championship. They'll be at the starting line in Kailua Bay next Saturday.

Let's go back a little more than twenty years. I was a 47 year old middle of the pack triathlete. I had raced my first triathlon ten years before that, and throughout those years I had always dreamed about doing the Hawaii Ironman … some day. But in my early years of racing, Ironman was just a dream for me. As much as I had always wanted to race it, the commitment to training, and the sheer magnitude of the event kept me away from it. For the first eight years, most of my triathlons were Sprint and Olympic distance races. In 1991, I decided to try some longer events. I finished the NYC Marathon and I began competing in half ironman distance triathlons. It was in 1992 that I started thinking seriously that racing Hawaii wasn't so unrealistic after all. And so began my two year plan.

Things really changed for me in February 1992 when I attended a weekend triathlon training clinic with Dave Scott, a six time Ironman Champion and the first inductee into the Ironman Hall of Fame. This was my second tri clinic with Dave Scott, and as anyone who knows Dave will tell you, he is very personable and approachable. At the end of the weekend I talked to Dave about my dreams to race Hawaii. He knew much of my training and racing background, but he asked me one important question. "Have you ever run a marathon?" A "yes" got me his encouragement and the "green light". On my training calendar he signed that day "Ironman 1994. Do it!"

And so I laid out a two-year plan with milestones which I felt I had to achieve on my critical path to the Ironman in Kona Hawaii in October 1994.

Today, there are thousands of men and women who have raced in one or more of the 39 Ironman triathlons around in the world, or they have a friend or relative who raced. But Hawaii still ranks as the best of them all - the Big Kahuna. It is the World Championship event and every triathlete's dream race. In the 1980's and early 1990's however, Hawaii was virtually all there was. And there were fewer athletes who attempted to race it. So my desire to race Ironman made me a rarity - a crazy rarity - at that time.

Let me set the stage here. In order to qualify to race in the Ironman Triathlon World Championship in Hawaii, an athlete must finish as a top athlete in his or her age division in a sanctioned Ironman Qualifier (IQ) triathlon. In the 1980's and 1990's, IQ races spanned the range from Olympic distance triathlons (1 mile swim / 24.8 mile / 6.2 mile run) through half iron distance triathlons (1.2 mile swim / 56 mile bike / 13.1 mile run). Today, as more ironman distance races have surfaced around the globe, the only sanctioned IQ races are ironman distance.

An additional way to qualify for a slot in Hawaii is through a limited Lottery. If an athlete is chosen in the Lottery he or she still must complete a sanctioned event before getting acceptance to race in Kona.

On May 2nd, 1994 I found out that I had been accepted through the Lottery to compete in Hawaii. That night my son Dave said "Dad, you should keep a journal to help you remember everything about this time in your life." This book is that journal. And it's more than that. It's a collection of my thoughts and experiences leading up to and including race day, as well as training and racing tips that worked (and sometimes didn't work) for me. I was self-trained at that time, and I used a lot of resources that were at my disposal to help me get to the finish line. (Later in 1995, Dave Scott did eventually become my coach after he retired from professional racing)

So this book is more than just a story. It's also meant to be a training tool. I hope you, the reader, will cull training tips, race preparation ideas, and other valuable advice about what you need to do to get ready for an Ironman distance race. Enjoy and learn.

Writing this book has turned out to be a lot of fun, resurrecting great memories from more than twenty years ago. I owe a lot of thanks to so many people who helped me and encouraged me throughout my training and racing. My son Dave was there at the start, encouraging me with his smile and the look of pride on his face. He welcomed me at the finish line of my first race and quickly decided to race the following year. Dave and I trained and raced side-by-side for many years, and Dave is now a competitive cyclist in his own right. Many thanks go out to my friends Mike and Barbara Marchev. Mike got me started with his March 1985 phone call and then he too raced an Ironman in the late '90's. Barbara and he also surprised me when they flew to Kona to support me in 1994. And I owe the most thanks to my wife Judy. She encouraged me from the very beginning to take on this crazy quest. She supported me all the way. She juggled social events with family and friends during my peak training months. She kept me on track and pushed me when I got tired or lazy. She made sure I got out of bed for the pre-dawn runs, massaged my aching muscles and my disappointed ego when things didn't go exactly as planned, and she never once complained. She was always there at every finish line.

Frank Adornato

Chapter One

How I Got The Tri Bug

In 1980 I was at my parents' house for Sunday dinner and ABC Wide World of Sports was covering the Hawaii Ironman for the first time. I remember watching what I thought was a completely crazy event. I had no idea what the Ironman was, but as the description unfolded in the telecast, I thought "These guys are nuts!" The idea of a 2.4 mile ocean swim, followed by a 112 mile bike, and then a full 26.2 marathon run was insanity. The craziness of the race was further enforced in my mind by the fact that the athletes were required to have their body weight checked throughout the race course to ensure that they weren't becoming dangerously dehydrated.

But when the program ended, I didn't see these athletes as a bunch of lunatics. I found myself envying their strength, stamina and discipline. I didn't know it at the time but every year when I watched the Ironman coverage on TV I was getting more and more drawn into the sport, until eventually I decided to do a triathlon myself.

It was March 1985. My friend Mike Marchev called me to tell me he was thinking of racing a local "TinMan" Triathlon in Bridgewater, New Jersey, and wouldn't it be fun if we trained and raced it together. The year before, we had heard about this new race. We had even considered going to watch it, but it rained. We never went because we were sure the race officials would cancel due to bad weather. Boy, were we naive!

Anyway, we decided to do the race which was scheduled for May 31st. That meant we had three months to prepare. Mike and I were both in reasonably good physical condition, but neither of us had been doing any real aerobic training since college. In my first training run I covered one mile in nine minutes, but I was done for the day. Ironically I was proud of the fact that I didn't stop to walk. But on race day I needed to run 5.2 more miles after having swum and cycled. When I jumped in the pool for my first training swim, I couldn't make it back and forth twice before I needing to stop for a breath. And forget about the bike. It had cobwebs on it. Boy did I have work to do!

So we trained. We swam at a local health club pool. We rode indoor bikes and ran on an indoor track in March. Once the snow melted and the roads cleared, we began cycling and running outdoors. Our typical training week was cycling 10 or more miles two to three times a week, running 3 miles three times a week, swimming 15 to 20 minutes three times a week, and lifting weights. We thought we had a structured training plan, but the sport of triathlon was in its infancy stage, and no one really knew how to prepare properly. In hindsight we were woefully undertrained!

Our goal for the race was to finish, to survive. The race distances were 1/3 mile lake swim, 23 miles bike and a 10K (6.2 mile) run. We didn't consider nor did we train for how hilly or flat the course was. We didn't think about finish times. And there was zero consideration about ever doing a second triathlon. By mid May - two weeks before race day - we had trained up to the race distances. We knew we could swim 1/2 mile; we could bike 23 miles; and we could run 6.2 miles. But could we do all three back-to-back?

A couple of weeks before race day Mike found out that he had to travel out of town on business so he was out of the race. He couldn't compete. He was disappointed. I was scared! Even though you race alone in the sport of triathlon, there had been some comfort knowing my buddy would be out there racing too. I started to have second thoughts about whether I had trained and prepared enough. (See I was learning fast!) My son Dave who was 14 years old, and several friends came along as a support crew. To this day, I'm convinced they really came to see how far I'd go before I dissolved into a sweating puddle.

On race morning, we arrived at the lake two hours early so that I could set up my transition gear, and re-set my transition gear, and re-set my transition gear again. I must have moved my stuff around at least twenty times. It's funny, but I still go through a similar ritual to this day (but not as obsessively), setting up my gear and mentally and physically going through the movements of my transition from the swim to the bike.

Walking to the beach before the race start didn't help my nerves either. The swim distance looked much longer than 1/3 mile. This observation was re-enforced by other athletes, all of whom were nervous triathlon virgins like me, and who were convinced the swim must be longer than advertised.

In reality, it was a 1/3 mile out-and-back swim, and the last half of the course went parallel to the shore in about three feet of water.

And so we were all beckoned to the sandy shore by the race official. We heard the usual announcements about sportsmanship and safety. We were divided into three waves, identified by swim cap color, and the starting gun was fired.

There are two things that I remember vividly about that swim. When I put my face in the lake water for the first time I was shocked to see dark green instead of the clear water I had become accustomed to training in pools. I couldn't see anything in front of me, and it took me serval moments to get comfortable in the green water. And towards the end of the swim there was one guy making forward movement in the shallow water, bent over at the waist, moving his arms as if he was swimming, but walking to the swim exit. I don't know if he thought he fooling anybody, or maybe just fooling himself.

So after the swim (swim - walk - swim for some) many of us ran into the locker room for a quick shower before the bike. After all, who would ever think to transition to the bike without a refreshing shower and new set of clothes! But there was one guy I knew from Scotland - Stuart - who was on a business trip in New Jersey and decided to race with us. While everybody else dispersed into the locker rooms to change, Stuart figured he'd save time by dropping his swimsuit and changing on the boardwalk al fresco. He got a few cat whistles and remarks, but he was gone on his bike in a flash.

The bike ride was hilly, slow, and I hurt. I rode a Sears bike that weighed about 40 pounds. My helmet was borrowed and aerobars hadn't been invented yet. Nothing was aerodynamic. Most of us wore running shoes, some with and some without toeclips on their bike pedals. About 1 1/2 hours later I got off my bike in the second transition area and I tried to stand on legs of rubber. I toweled off the sweat (there were no showers available), changed shirts, ate half a banana, drank some water, and tried to convince myself that I had invested too much time and energy to quit now.

As I started the run I got my first doubts about my ability to finish. My legs were painfully tight. I felt like I was running like a duck - a very slow duck. Unknown to me, a good friend from work, Bob Michalak was watching the race. Bob was a ranked college runner so a 10K run was no problem for him. Bob jumped into the run course and ran along side of me for a few miles, giving me moral support to help me keep going. My legs did loosen up a little after the first mile, and I walked at each water aid station. And with each mile marker my confidence grew. After I passed the half way marker I knew I'd finish and my pace quickened. I completed that race in 2 hours 26 minutes. Not an impressive finish, but I finished with my head up. I crossed the finish line with a full sense of accomplishment. I remember seeing the smile of pride on my son's face as he congratulated me, and the next thought that went through my mind was NEVER AGAIN!

Obviously I did compete again. The next year. 1986, my son completed his first triathlon at TinMan. For many years thereafter, we trained and raced together. Well, we'd start together, and he'd blow by me early in the bike portion of the race and wait for me at the finish line. Over the next few years we raced Sprints and Olympic distance triathlons, plus some 10K runs and duathlons. And all the time Ironman was always there. A dream, out of reach for me. Or so I thought.

Chapter Two

I Am A Triathlete

People get into the sport of triathlon for many reasons. Some want to prove something to themselves or use it as a way to get over their mid-life crisis. Some compete to win, others consider it a victory just to finish.

When I started training for my first triathlon in 1985 I had no idea what an impact the sport would have on my life. I really thought I would do that one race and that would be it. But the training got me into such excellent condition I decided to continue. Training and racing in triathlons kept me healthy and fit. It was a lifestyle choice. But even after I continued to compete for some time, I considered myself someone "who competed in the sport of triathlon". I didn't consider myself someone who was good enough to say the words "I am a triathlete".

I recall several separate conversations at parties or other social events. If someone learned that I had raced in triathlons they often asked if I had raced in ".. that crazy race in Hawaii. You know, the Ironman?" "No. Just the short stuff." I'd say. But deep down, I wished I could say "Yes".

In my third or fourth year of racing, I had a training partner who always talked about wanting to race in Hawaii. (I kept my dreams to myself. While I wanted to race there, I didn't think it would ever happen. So why bring it up?) Somehow he got a photocopy of the Ironman Entry Form, and we talked about whether or not he should send it in. It was a simple one page form, and we didn't even know if it was the real deal or if it would have been accepted as a valid application. He never sent it in, and unfortunately he eventually lost interest in racing. The last time I saw him he had gained a lot of weight and dropped out of the race scene completely.

After I had been competing for about a four or five years I realized that my race pace was getting very predictable. Before every race, I could predict within minutes what my actual finish time would be. My training was in a rut; I needed a training boost. It was about that time that I saw an ad for a week long Triathlon Training Clinic in Texas Hill Country near Austin. In February 1990 I flew to Texas for one week of intensive training, and some fun, with triathlon legends like Dave Scott, Ray Browning, Paula Newby Frazier, and John Howard. There were about a dozen of us, and we spent most of our waking hours swimming, cycling, running, eating, sleeping and learning about triathlon. We swam every day, we did 7 am runs, rain or shine, and a lot of windy and hilly bike rides. At the end of the week I had learned volumes about training smart. Later that year my race finish times improved tremendously, and at a sprint race in Pennsylvania, I got a 3rd place podium finish in my age group. Finally I felt comfortable saying "I am a triathlete".

As the years went by and I continued to race, I still finished mostly in the middle of the pack, but every once in a while the stars aligned for me and my performance was good enough for a podium finish. Ironman was still out there in my mind, and I guess I was starting to think maybe it might happen. In early 1991, I made the decision to train for and race the New York City Marathon. While I didn't verbalize it to anyone, I knew it was a first personal test to see if I had the stamina for long distance racing.

I ran the New York City Marathon in November 1991. Although I felt that I had trained properly for the 26.2 mile distance, the race beat me to a pulp. I tried to maintain a 9 minute pace per mile, which was based upon what my training runs told me I could do. But it wasn't going to happen that day. To this day I don't know why. I was a novice, a first timer. And I can only guess that I just wasn't mentally prepared for the toll that race distance takes on the human body. As I crossed the finish line and saw the clock, all I could think was NEVER AGAIN. My finish time was 4 hours 08 minutes. That's about a 9:30 pace. A little off my target but as I now realize, not too bad. But boy, did my body hurt. Later I counted nine blisters on my feet,. I lost several toe nails and it took a few days before walking down steps didn't cause me to flinch with pain. And then selective memory set in. I remembered the elation of finishing my first marathon and I forgot about the pain. I knew that with better training, I could race faster and better. I was happy with that. But what was more important to me was that I was starting to think that Ironman was more than a just a dream. Maybe Ironman was a possibility for me.

NYC Marathon 1995. My third marathon and my first finish under 4 hours.

Chapter Three

The Plan

It was Christmas time 1991. I was enjoying some holiday rest and recovery after the NYC Marathon. I read in Triathlete Magazine that there was another triathlon clinic coming up in Boston in February. It was only a weekend clinic, mostly classroom seminars with a little gym work, but Dave Scott was the featured speaker. We went.

At the end of the last day, I walked up to Dave and asked him about Ironman. By now I knew I wanted to do it, but I didn't know how realistic it was for me. I was approaching 50, but I felt that I was in pretty good shape, regardless of my age. What did he think? We talked some about my recent training and racing, and then he asked me one key question. Have you ever run a marathon? Yes I have. I did NYC three months ago in a little over 4 hours. Is that good enough? That answer got me his encouragement and the "green light". But when to race? I didn't think my schedule in 1993 would allow me adequate time to train and prepare myself properly, so I tentatively chose 1994. Dave Scott signed my training calendar "Ironman 1994. Do it!"

On the drive home from Boston, Judy and I talked the entire way about Ironman. Judy was 100% in support of my goal. She had always supported my racing, having come to cheer me on in virtually every race I ever did. Now we were going to prepare for this one – the Hawaii Ironman - together.

Next we talked about timing. The time commitment for training was going to be huge. We talked about other obligations and plans for the upcoming two years to make sure that we weren't biting off more than we could chew, The only major project that we had on our calendar was a new house. We had started the plans to build a new house which would keep us busy until early 1993. So Ironman 1993 wasn't realistic – but 1994 looked like a good year. And so the date was set.

I knew I needed to schedule a series of training races as well as mandatory Ironman qualifying races in 1993 and 1994, and I wanted to race another marathon in 1993. These would allow me to continue to build my distance base and give me a reading on my mental and physical stamina at longer distances. Another important thing we agreed we wanted was to go to Kona, Hawaii and watch the 1993 race and learn. A spectacular vacation with an agenda.

But the proof is in the details, and I needed to work on details.

I had heard and read so many horror stories about the difficulties training for an Ironman. Some have said that the grueling months of training are worse than the race itself. (An observation that proved to be true for me.) I wanted to be sure that I was properly prepared come race day.

When we got home from Boston, I sat down and charted out a plan with specific milestones along the way. Like the race itself, the training program needed to be divided into manageable pieces. I planned to compete in a lot of races during the next eighteen months, but there were several key milestone races that I needed to achieve. Each milestone would bring me closer to the end goal of being physically and mentally prepared to race the Hawaii Ironman on October 15th, 1994.

The plan that I laid out for myself was:

• July 1992. Tupper Lake Half Ironman. Goal: Finish.
• July 1993. Tupper Lake Half Ironman. Goal: Faster than 1992. (Under 6 hours)
• October 1993. Go to Kona. Watch the race. Goal: See the event first hand and learn as much as possible about race logistics. Swim, bike and run on part of the actual course and visualize the course in my training back home.
• November 1993. NYC Marathon. Goal: Under 4 hours.
• Winter 1993-1994. Work with a swim coach to improve swim stroke and speed.
• March 1994. Be able to swim 3 miles at race pace (30 minutes a mile)
• March 1994. Send in my application to race Kona 1994. Schedule Ironman Qualifier races for the season.
• April 1994. St. Anthony's Triathlon St. Petersburg Florida. First IM Qualifier of the season.
• July 1994. Be able to swim, bike and run Ironman distances individually.
• July 1994. Tupper Lake Half Ironman. Goal: Beat my 1993 time.

Admittedly some of these milestones carried more weight than others. The most critical of all in my mind were the half ironman distance events and the visit to Kona. These, I felt, would tell me how strong I was - and how strong I needed to be - to face the challenge of training and of race day.

From these experiences, I would learn things about myself that were crucially important to a successful Ironman – some good and some not so good. The plan for Ironman 1994 was in place, but there was a lot of work yet to do.

Chapter Four

The Training

This is probably a good place for me to explain my philosophy and outlook on triathlon racing and especially racing the Ironman.

Obviously it takes an enormous amount of physical training to prepare your body for the distances involved. Anyone who thinks it's easy, is very wrong.

I can't tell you how many friends and acquaintances have told me over the years that they were pretty sure they could do an Ironman. One guy (who will remain nameless) told me many times that he could race an Ironman. He could easily cover the swim and bike. The marathon might be tough for him, but he was sure that he could finish an Ironman. Well one day, after I had raced Kona twice and other ironman races as well, when that guy and his wife were visiting Judy and me at our condo in Kona, he and I went for a swim in Kailua Bay. We didn't set a time or distance; it was just going to be a fun swim on part of the ironman swim course. We started on "Dig Me" beach where the Ironman swim starts and went off at an easy pace. After about five minutes, when we reached the end of the Pier, he stopped and with bated breath, he asked me how far had we gone into the race course. I told him we were at the starting line. The look of disbelief on his face was priceless. We returned back to the beach and he never again mentioned how "easy" it would be for him to race Ironman.

So we can agree that training takes time and effort, and that you need to prepare your body for the distance and pressures of the race. That's a given fact. In addition however, with the physical training comes self-confidence and the knowledge that you can do it. In order to have a good race, you need to know without a doubt that your body can perform in the swim, bike and run for the long distances and many hours that are required to reach the finish line. There are no shortcuts. When you're treading water at the starting line you need to know that you have prepared well and you're ready to race.

If you train correctly, the conditions of the race should not be new to you on race day. Your training should make you mentally and physically familiar with everything (or as much as possible) that you will experience on that day, and it should be almost second nature for your mind and body to respond and re-act to what's happening to you.

As you go through your workout sessions, think about what, when and where you might be during the race, and think about how your body is handling what-ever situation you are in at that time. For example, most of my swim training was in a pool. But knowing that open water presents different challenges, I tried to work on certain techniques to prepare for open water swims. First, I learned to breathe bilaterally, i.e., inhaling alternately on both my left side and my right side. Bilateral breathing helps with open water navigation, and it also helps prevent dizziness in longer swims. Also, I took every opportunity I could to swim in open water - lakes, bays, and the ocean.

Another example is experimenting with the foods and drinks I would consume on the bike and in the run. During training rides and runs, I tried different sports drinks in addition to water, Power Bars and a variety of fruits, so I knew what would sit well in my stomach without causing GI problems.

As an interesting side note, carbohydrate gels had not yet become commercially available in the early 1990's. However, during the run portion of the 1994 Ironman race we were offered a carbohydrate gel in an unlabeled pouch. I was hesitant to try it, but I was hungry and exhausted and I was in the last few miles of the marathon. So I took a pouch tried it. Luckily it worked well, and I have used gels ever since for all my long rides and runs as well as races.

And last, if it's at all practical, visit the race site weeks or months before the actual race. Go over the race course. Swim, bike and run all or part of the route. If that's not possible, at least drive the course in your car. Look for landmarks and become familiar with the layout and terrain. Are the roads flat? hilly? any blind curves on the bike? Etc. Then when you get back home, picture yourself on the race course when you're training on your home turf.

These techniques and experiences will help to minimize the unknowns on race day. No surprises.

The bottom line is NOTHING NEW ON RACE DAY. The clothes you wear on race day, the gear you use, the food and liquids that you eat and drink - everything - should be tried and tested in training.

And another note. The day before most races, there usually is a race expo with vendors showcasing and selling their products. At Ironman they showcase and sell everything sports related: swim suits, swim goggles, bikes and cycling equipment of all types, running shoes, clothing and sports foods and drinks, to name a few. If you want to buy something new at the expo, DO NOT wear it or use it during the race. Take it home and use it first in training. to make sure it works well for you. Something as simple as a new pair of swimming goggles can ruin your swim. Trust me. I learned the hard way. In 2000, I was in Panama City Beach, Florida to race Ironman Florida. At the expo, they were demonstrating a new style of swim goggles with a wider field of vision. I tried a pair in my training swim and liked them. I liked them so much that I bought a pair, and without thinking, I wore them for the race the next day. I wasn't ten strokes into the swim when the entire Gulf of Mexico started to leak into my goggles! It was too early in the swim to stop to fix them; I would have been swum over by the mass of swimmers behind me. So I swam for a long time with my eyes stinging from the salt water. Eventually when the swim pack thinned out enough, I stopped to tread water and fix the seal of the goggles on my face. It worked fine for a while but then they started leaking again. This happened for the entire 2.4 mile swim. I would swim a distance, stop, readjust my goggles and continue until they leaked again. Only to repeat the same thing over and over again. A miserable swim!

Now back to the real training story. As I entered the spring of 1992, my Ironman strategy was in place. Now all I and to do was execute the plan.

In May I started the race season with my usual standard, The Garden State TinMan Triathlon. Since this was the race that started it all for me, it was a sentimental favorite. And since it was the same course every year, I could compare my finish times to previous years and get a reading on my early season fitness level. The TinMan Triathlon was a very good barometer of my race fitness level. That year I finished with a new personal best of 2 hours 8 minutes. I was well on my way. But the next race, a major milestone race, was still ahead of me, and I didn't appreciate what an eye opener it would be.

The Tupper Lake Half Ironman Triathlon is held each year in mid July. Tupper Lake is a very small village in New York State in the Adirondack Mountains about an hour northwest of Lake Placid, NY. It had been an Ironman qualifier in previous years, but not in 1992. Between the hills, the altitude and northwest latitude of the town, it's almost always a cool race venue. The swim as you might guess is held in Tupper Lake, where the water temperature seems to never get above the 60 degree range. The 56 mille bike is on a rolling out-and-back course on beautiful country roads, and the 13.1 mile run goes through the village and onto secluded wooded trails. It too is an out-and-back route with a long steep uphill climb at the start, but with the saving grace of a downhill to the finish line.

Since this was to be the longest triathlon I had done to date, my major focus was making sure that I put in enough miles on the bike. The race distances for the half ironman race are 1.2 miles swim / 56 miles bike / 13.1 miles run. I was comfortable with my swimming, and since completing the marathon the previous November, I had maintained a good running base. But my bike mileage was not optimal. In fact it was low in the 35 to 40 mile range. I did work myself up to long rides over 65 miles, but I didn't spend enough training time doing long distance bike to run "bricks" where you ride and then transition immediately to a long run. And I paid big time for that omission!

The race was being held on Sunday July 18th, and Judy and I arrived in Tupper Lake the Friday before race day. We had booked a room in the 3/30 Motel which is neither on Route 3 nor Route 30, but it's walking distance to the lake. Funny story… when I called to book the room, I asked if they had non-smoking rooms. (Remember this was 1992 and non-smoking rooms weren't as commonplace as they are today.) After a brief pause the young women on the phone said "You don't have to smoke in the room if you don't want to." !!!

On the drive to Tupper lake, it had rained for the entire 6 hours and the rain held on through the night. Saturday morning was cool and cloudy, but the rain had stopped. Following my own advice about eliminating as many unknowns as possible before the race, we spent part of Saturday familiarizing ourselves with the race course. We drove the entire bike route and the on-road portion of the run course.

I also followed my usual routine of a very short, very easy workout in all three events on the day prior too the race. So I cycled and ran easy on parts of the course, and I swam a little in lake. The water was very cool, clear, and flat.

After an early dinner, Judy and I took a short walk and went to bed.

We were up before dawn on Sunday. The weather had not improved much over the previous few days. It was cool, cloudy and a light rain fell intermittently. We walked down to the lake, I found my transition spot, and went through my pre-race ritual of setting my bike and run gear so that everything was where I wanted it to be for fast, smooth transitions from swimmer to cyclist and then later in the day, from cyclist to runner. I put on my swim wetsuit and jumped in the lake for a warm-up swim. The water actually felt warmer than on Saturday, until I got out of the lake and realized that was because the air temperature was cooler than the water. The swim start was divided into several waves of swimmers for better safety. As I waited for my swim wave to be called for the start of the race I was shivering and anxious to get started. The weatherman had predicted better conditions for later in the morning, and as it turned out he wasn't wrong. The rain stopped when the first wave of swimmers hit the water at 8 am. My wave went off at 8:15 and my swim time was pretty good at 35:27.

After a reasonably fast transition, delayed only by the time it took to get out of the wetsuit, I was off on the bike. By design, I stayed in a low gear and spun my legs fast to get the blood flowing after the cool water swim. It took a few miles before that happened and then I was good to go. In the end however, I wasn't all that happy with my bike split of 3 hours 15 minutes, but the worst was yet to come.

As luck would have it, the clouds parted and the sun broke through just as I finished my bike to run transition. I was feeling disappointed in my poor bike split and my quads felt like lead. I shuffled through the first half mile, a flat stretch by the edge of the lake. The runners then took a sharp left turn for a steep 2 mile climb up Main Street. By the time I got to the top of that hill I felt wasted, my head was burning hot from the sun, and with eleven miles yet to go, I started making up excuses in my head about why I should quit and call it a day. I decided to keep going, barely holding onto a 9 minute pace per mile, which I calculated would get me a 6 hour finish. That pace fell apart around mile 6. The course had gone off road at about mile 4, which was a partial blessing because of the shade that the trees provided. But keeping a steady pace became more and more difficult. Had it not been for the 2 mile downhill on Main Street, I probably would have done much worse than 6 hours 10 minutes.

As I ran for the finish I was as close to exhaustion as I'd ever been. I crossed the finish line, staggered over to the nearest tree and collapsed in the shade. When Judy ran over to see if I was OK, all I could think to say was NEVER AGAIN! There was no way I would ever do another half ironman distance race again, and forget about the Ironman!

Packing up my gear, showering and getting ready for dinner, I kept thinking about my training. Obviously I was doing something wrong, or maybe just not doing enough of whatever it was that's the right thing to do. By later that evening, or maybe it was the next morning, selective memory clicked in, and I started thinking about how I had to improve my training in order to race better next year.

I ended 1992 with a few shorter triathlons and a resolution to work on an improved training plan for 1993.

With the anguish of my poor finish (a melt down really) at Tupper Lake still in the back of my mind, I started the 1993 training season re-building my running base. I worked hard on my running without ignoring my cycling and swimming. I concentrated on building my long distance runs and increasing the distance of my speed sets. My first test came in early May. I ran the Broad Street Run, a 10 mile flat and fast race in Philadelphia. I finished in 75 minutes 15 seconds, which was a personal best for that distance. My finish time at The Garden State TinMan later in May was 2 hours 11 minutes. Just 3 minutes off my personal best the previous year.

And then came Tupper Lake again. This time I was ready. I had changed my training style, and my run and bike workouts felt stronger and faster. But would the more intense workouts pay off? Conditions in 1993 were a little better than the previous year. Still cool, but no rain. I clicked in at 5 hours 52 minutes .. a full 18 minutes faster than 1992. The time savings came off of both the bike and the run. When I crossed the finish line that year I danced to the rock music being played. I was on an emotional high and I felt great.

The next major milestone was the trip to Kona, Hawaii to train on the course, to watch and to learn as many intricate details as I could about the Hawaii Ironman World Championship Triathlon.

Judy and I flew to Maui first for some vacation, and that helped us get accustomed to the six hour time difference before we flew to the Big Island. When we got to the Maui airport for the short 40 minute flight to Kona, there were several athletes there with us waiting for the flight. I was surprised that these athletes were arriving in Kona so late in the week since there is so much preparation to do before the race. It's much better to plan to arrive early in the week or on the weekend beforehand if you can afford the time. (More about that later.)

Wednesday was spent walking around town and soaking in all that was going on. A large grandstand was being set up at the finish line on Alii Drive, NBC cameramen and reporters were everywhere, as were the 1500 Ironman athletes swimming, biking and running in their pre-race preparation. I went for two morning swims on Thursday and Friday, and I ran part of Alii Drive. The intense heat was immediately evident everywhere we went.

We also drove the full bike course up to Hawi and back. What I learned from that ride was that there is a long stair step climb for about 10+ miles up to the bike turn-around in the town of Hawi on the northwest point of the Big Island. I would be cycling up that hill about 35 miles into the bike portion of the race. If the wind was in my face, which was a distinct possibility, I would be riding low gears, slow and steady.

On Saturday, race day, we were up at 5 am for the swim start. At 7 am the cannon fired and 1500 adrenaline filled athletes started their long day in a mass swim start. We volunteered to work at an aid station on the Queen K, at mile 15 of the marathon, which was also about mile 90 of the bike course. This gave us a good vantage point to watch the middle of the pack cyclists coming in at a late stage of their ride, as well as the runners. Again, we couldn't help but be aware of the heat and wind out there. It was exhausting and were just standing around handing out water and Gatorade to the athletes. As we were out there on the Queen K and all day long, I kept thinking about me racing in Kona next year. I was excited, but at the same time, I remembered the proverb: "Be careful what you wish for because you just might get it."

We were relieved of our volunteer duties about dinner time so we went back into town and hung out at the finish line until midnight when the last triathlete crossed over and was told "You are an Ironman".

On Sunday morning, I got up early with the plan to do a long run out on the Queen K. Since I had the New York City Marathon coming up in a month, I needed to get in a scheduled long run, plus I wanted the experience of running out in the lava fields. Short story. I didn't make ten miles running. I completely underestimated the heat, even so very early in the morning. My training run deteriorated down to a jog, walk, jog I had used up all my water half way through the run. I staggered into the hotel lobby and was grateful to get back to my air conditioned room.

Those four days were a wide span of emotions for me. It was inspiring, exciting, and scary. But most importantly, it was extremely helpful in my Ironman preparation. That visit gave me a long list of things to do over the next twelve months. Physical and mental training, and a checklist of do's and don'ts that I probably would not have known about had we not gone on that trip. The most important benefit to me was that I had seen the entire course and I had a sampling of the conditions, terrain, and weather which I could expect in 1994. I could now visualize myself on the race course while I trained on my home turf over the next twelve months.

I finished 1993 with my last milestone, the New York City Marathon. That went well too. I was hyped from having been to Kona a month before, and I ran well. More important was that I felt fine after the race. I wasn't exhausted like I had been in 1991. I felt like my body had crested another level, and I was ready to begin training for the 1994 Ironman.

As was my plan, I enrolled with a swim coach at the local YMCA in December 1993. Since I expected that running and cycling outdoors would be limited by snowy roads, I focused heavily on improving my swim stroke and efficiency that winter. As it turned out, this worked well for me since the winter of 1993-1994 went down in the record books as one of the snowiest winters on the northeast coast. The first snow fell on January 7th and it snowed once or twice every week through March. The road surfaces didn't re-appear again until April. Running was limited almost completely to the treadmill, and wind trainers were the order of the day for cycling.

In addition to the once a week swim sessions with my coach, I spent two other evenings a week doing intervals and distance workouts. By early March I was swimming about 10,000 yards a week, including 5000 yards sets (10 x 500's) every other week.

A review of my training log reminded me that I hadn't done any real distance cycling during the entire winter. Because the roads were so icy, I hadn't been outside on a bike through the month of March. My longest run in those winter months was limited to 10 miles. But in early April, as soon as the weather broke, I was outside working on my cycling and running again.

Another thing that I did in March was to send in my Ironman entry application. While I wanted to qualify through racing, I doubled down on my chances by entering the Ironman Lottery. In the '90's there were two ways to get into the Ironman race. Either you had to place high in your age group in a sanctioned Ironman Qualifier (IQ) triathlon or you could enter the Lottery and hope that your name was pulled. If your name was picked in the Lottery, you still needed to show evidence that you completed an IQ race.

The list of sanctioned IQ races came out in March, and I setup a training and racing schedule so I could race as many IQ triathlons as possible in order to maximize my chances for an entry slot in October. Actually I worked out a dual schedule for the year.

Plan A was to race in IQ's until August, or until I earned a slot for Kona, whichever came first. If I failed to get a slot for Kona, my backup for Plan A was to race in a small local iron distance triathlon in Clermont Florida targeted for the week after Kona. (I didn't want to waste all of my training and not race the distance. Clermont is not an official Ironman event and therefore it was relatively easy to sign up and race. It still exists as one of the best grass-roots iron distance events held every October, one week after the Kona race.)

Plan B was to switch over to local races as soon as I was entered into Kona either from qualifying in an IQ race or through the Lottery. The reasons for Plan B were practical. If I didn't need to do more IQ's I could race locally and save money and vacation time for the trip to Hawaii.

No sooner was the spring thaw upon us, it was time to fly to St. Petersburg, Florida for the race season opener - St. Anthony's Olympic Distance Triathlon. Steeped in a lot of tradition, St. Anthony's was the first Ironman Qualifying race of the season, held that year on Sunday April 24th. The 1.5 K swim was held in the Vinoy Basin of Tampa Bay. The 40 K bike was flat but with a lot of turns through the residential areas of St. Petersburg. And the 10 K run, also mostly flat, hugs the bay, offering a very scenic run to the finish line back at Vinoy Park.

When Judy and I arrived in St. Pete on the Friday afternoon before the race, the weather was warm and the skies were clear. It felt so good to be in a tropical climate after such a cold, snowy, miserable winter. After checking into our hotel, unpacking our suitcases, and assembling my bike, we walked around town, picked up my race packet at the expo, and checked out the race transition areas. Because it was the first IQ race of the season, St. Anthony's drew a very large field of competitors from around the United States, as well as a large field of professional triathletes. St. Petersburg was curb to curb with superbly fit and toned athletes. For me this was both exciting and daunting. Did I belong in this crowd? (Even today, in spite of the fact that St. Anthony's is no longer an IQ race, it continues to draw a large field of several thousand competitors.)

On Saturday morning before breakfast, I did my usual pre-race workout consisting of a low gear, easy spin on the bike, an easy jog with several "fast feet" pick ups, and an easy stroke swim in the bay. That morning the bay was smooth and calm. But that was not to be on race day.

The swim course started at Spa Beach next to the famous St. Pete Pier. The course went straight out in the bay parallel to the Pier. From there it made several counter-clockwise turns into the open bay, eventually ending into the smooth waters of Vinoy Basin and out of the water into Transition number 1. On Sunday morning at 7 am, we all started the swim in reasonably calm waters, but as soon as we reached the open waters at the end of the Pier the choppy waves hit us hard. The chops were so bad - for me at least - that they made breathing and navigation a challenge. I exited the water in 33 minutes, a full three minutes slower than planned. The bike was uneventful, but with so many turns, it was difficult for me to get into a fast rhythm. I got off the bike in 1 hr 13 minutes. (20.3 mph average.) Not bad, but not a PR for me for 40K. And I ran the 10K in 52 minutes flat. Again, not bad, but not great. Bottom line, my overall time of 2 hr 44:50 was not good enough to garner me a slot in Hawaii. But at least now I had completed my first IQ race.

We were back at home on Tuesday, and my training resumed in earnest after a few days recovery.

Then on May 2nd, I got the news! My name was chosen in the Ironman Lottery, and with the St. Anthony's finish already under my belt, I was in! No more "fooling around". Now it was for real. I had about five months left to train and prepare both physically and mentally for the big race in October. Plan B it was.

Training six days a week, my schedule was to run and swim on Mondays, Wednesdays and Saturdays, and to bike and do strength work on Tuesdays, Thursdays, and Sundays. Fridays were my recovery days. In July I started doing a bike to run brick workout every weekend. I also made it a point to run or bike midday once or twice a week. Working out in the midday heat helped acclimatize my body and prepare for the grueling heat in Hawaii.

This is the second time I've mentioned "brick" workouts, so for the uninitiated I guess it would help if I explained. A brick workout is doing two disciplines back-to-back during the same workout, one after the other with minimal to no interruption in between. Technically a brick can be a bike to run, swim to bike, swim to run, or any combination of the two. However, the most common brick is the bike to run, probably because that's the transition that causes the most pain and discomfort to the legs. I started with shorter distance bricks - 20 mile bike followed by a 3 mile run - and increased every other week. My longest single brick in training was a 100 mile bike, followed immediately by a 30 minute run. Some coaches argue that the run portion of the brick doesn't need to be more than 30 minutes since the goal of the brick workout is to train your quadriceps and hamstrings to switch from short, concentric contractions on the bike to elongated eccentric contractions on the run, and this occurs usually in just a few minutes.

By the end of July I had done two 100 mile rides, and my long runs were back at 20 miles. I was swimming about 10,000 yards a week, including one continuous 5000 yard swim every few weeks.

In August I swam 90 minutes in Barnagat Bay to test my ability at the 2.4 mile distance in open water. It went just as I had hoped and planned.

My training also included two half ironman distance races at Clermont, Florida and Tupper Lake, NY. For both races, I brought in finish times in the high 5-hour range, but more important to me was the fact that I was not flat-lining at the finish. I had more energy left in the tank at the end of 70.3 miles. But the question still remained. Could I do double the distance and race 140.6 miles?

With Ironman race day on October 15th, I worked to maximize my total week-ly mileage in August and early September. This would allow me to start a gradual pre-race taper in mid September. The goal of the taper is to be in peak physical condition on race morning. Peak condition translates to the perfect blend of fitness, rest and fuel (nutrition). A proper taper can be a tricky thing to do right. You want your body to be optimally rested in the days and weeks leading up to the race, but you do not want your body to get stale. You need to be fully hydrated and fed with the right foods. But not over-hydrated (to the point of electrolyte deficiencies) not over fed (to the point of weight gain or GI distress).

On September 19th, I started to gradually reduce the volume and intensity of my workouts. In the beginning this was very subtle, but by early October, my mileage was noticeably reduced from July and August. I continued my higher intensity workouts (speed drills and hill repeats) but the higher heart rate seg-ments were shorter and the rest intervals were longer.

Preparations were almost done. All that was left to do was things like prepare my gear checks lists, get a bike tune-up, and pack for the trip to Hawaii.

It All Comes To Pass. The Trip To Kona.

My Journal

As I mentioned at the start, everything I have written in this book has been culled from my notes in the journal (*in italics*) that I kept during this fantastic personal adventure. For this part of the story however, I decided to use my journal notes mostly verbatim.

Judy and I had asked my son Dave if he wanted to join us on the trip to Hawaii. He didn't have to answer; the smile said it all. Dave was a photographer with the Courier News at the time, and he pre-arranged for an Ironman Press Pass which would give him access on all parts of the race course.

And so the final steps of the journey begin.

Friday October 9th.

The staff at work threw a great "Good Luck" party for me. Everyone is in my corner. I was surprised but so pleased when Barbara (Marchev) told me that she and Mike would be flying to Kona to cheer me on.

(Barbara was my secretary and her unofficial job was to juggle my meeting calendar so that I could get in a lunch time workout most days of the week, and her husband Mike was the one who called me that infamous day in March 1985 and started this whole crazy quest!)

Yesterday I packed my bike and racing wheels. All of my clothes have been ready for days now. I've laid out my training clothes and gear; as well as my race day clothes. Saturday morning can't arrive soon enough. Last night we watched the NBC coverage of Ironman '93. My anxiety is turning into worry. My biggest fear is that I might become one of the unlucky 5% who don't finish. Athletes who make it to go to Kona for this race are so well trained that the finish rate is always in the 95% range. But there's that unlucky 5%. I know I've trained properly and enough, but watching the medics carry Christian Bustros off in a stretcher doesn't help convince me.

(Christian Bustros was a pro triathlete from Chile who came close to winning the race in 1992, only to be carried off the course the next year.)

Our flight tomorrow is at 6:00 am so we need to get to bed early. It's gonna be a long travel day.

Saturday October 8th.

I slept pretty well last night, but we were all awake at 3:00 am, way too early for our drive to the airport at 4:30 am. The flight out of Newark Airport left on time at 6:00 am and things went smoothly with our connections at Dallas Forth-Worth. I hope that my bike, wheels, and gear made it onto the plane as easily as we did. I'm feeling relaxed on the plane. I met a few other triathletes at the airport and talking with them and sharing stores helped to relax me.

Our arrival in Honolulu was on schedule, but my nerves were coming to the surface again. Mark Allen, Julie Moss and their young son are sitting in the row behind us on the inter-island flight to Kona. The plane is filled almost exclusively with triathletes and their families. Adrenaline is running high. Everybody's chatting and excited.

As we're in the air and approaching the Kailua-Kona airport, my heart is pounding with excitement. As we touch down on the runway, we're rolling parallel to the Queen K Highway and the lava fields which are right next to the runway, and my nervousness immediately subsides. The Big Island seems to have a calming effect.

Later on when I mentioned this to other people, many said the same thing, and every time I would come back to the Big Island in the future, I would feel that same calming effect upon landing in Kona.

Collected our luggage. My bike made it in one piece! The taxi ride to town was a quick fifteen minutes, and we checked into the King Kam Hotel and were in our room right away. The King Kam Hotel is the host hotel for ironman and it's located immediately next to the Pier. A very good location for the race. We took a short walk along Alii Drive, ate a light dinner and we were in bed by 9 pm, trying not to think about the fact that it was 3 am Eastern Time.

Sunday, October 9th.

I woke up about 5:40. I had slept well, but I stayed in bed until 6:15. After stretching and eating half a banana, I walked down to Dig Me Beach and swam easy for 20 minutes. There were some swells, but all-in-all I felt pretty good.

After a shower and breakfast, I checked my bike and went for a low gear, high rpm 20 mile ride on the Queen K. I didn't want to push big gears yet. With all of the athletes out on the Queen K hammering their rides, it wasn't easy to maintain my target pace. I worked to maintain a comfortable 17 mph speed. The ride north was easy with a tail wind, but there was strong wind in my face on the return. This was my first lesson about the cycling on The Big Island. It could be kind, but it was daunting.

Following lunch we spent a few hours relaxing poolside, after which I ran 35 minutes on Alii Drive. I timed today's run to coincide in the afternoon hours when I would be running race day on Alii Drive.

Another early dinner and in bed by 10 pm.

Monday, October 10th.

Up and out at 6:15. I was swimming with a pack of pre-race athletes. I swam for 30 minutes, a little stronger than yesterday. The water was calm and crystal clear. There are fish everywhere and the occasional green turtle - called Honu in Hawaii. With all of the sea life it's tough to keep track of time. Beautiful!

After my swim, I hung out at the Ironman information tent, meeting more athletes including Paula Newby-Frasier and Greg Welch. Everybody is so friendly. The tide charts at the info tent show that it will be low tide at 7 am on race day. Should be a good swim.

Today was the first day for race packet pick-up. I got my bag right after breakfast. Race number 621. I saw my name in print on the official race participant list. This is real!!

Later in the morning, Judy and I drove up to Waikoloa, a village about 15 miles north of Kona. This is one of the observation spots where Judy and friends will be waiting for me to pass them on the bike - if they can get there on time. We drove on one of the back roads to get there, knowing that the Queen K will be closed on race day.

I should interject here that the main road on the west side of the Big Island is the Queen Kaahumanu Highway (called the Queen K by locals), and since that is the main road for the Ironman bike course, it is closed to all traffic except race vehicles. Actually, most of the west and northwest side of the Big Island are closed for Ironman. The vast majority of residents in the Kona area fully embrace the Ironman spirit. Many roads are closed or restricted to traffic, many businesses close for the day, and thousands volunteer every year to help out for all or part of the race. It is truly a community event.

So with the Queen K closed and other roads restricting traffic, families and friends of athletes need to be creative in their transportation if they want see and cheer on their athletes on different parts of the race course. Trying to approximate when an athlete will ride or run at a certain point on the course and coordinating that with back road routes can be very challenging. But dozens of supporters do it every year. You would think they'd rather just sit by the pool and drink a Mai Tai!

After our stop at Waikoloa, we went on the Spenser Park which is near the end of the Queen K and at the start of the stair step climb to the bike turn-around at Hawi. I biked the re-maining 20 miles up to Hawi. The hills them-selves weren't too bad, but the ride was tough due to the head winds. At one point I was cy-cling on a mild rise, almost a false flat section, maintaining 85+ rpm cadence on the pedals. I looked down at my cyclometer and saw that I was barely going 14 mph. That's a head wind!

Judy met me in Hawi where we had lunch before heading back to Kona. On the way back, we drove through the Natural Energy Lab, which is a two-mile stretch off the Queen K and down to the ocean. This road is the turn-around point for the marathon and because it sits in a valley adjacent to the water, it tends to be hotter and more humid than conditions on the Queen K. Although I didn't run the road today, I walked a short distance and the heat and humidity drenched my shirt after only a few minutes.

Back in Kona we freshened up, had an early dinner and I was in bed again by 10 pm. But not before getting a relaxing leg massage from Judy. I slept very well.

Tuesday, October 11th.

We "slept in" today … until 6:30. I was a little slower getting started this morn-ing. I decided this would be a good day to eat what I planned to eat on race morning and follow that with a swim. I had fruit yogurt, a banana and a slice of whole wheat bread - my typical pre-race breakfast. We got down to the beach about 7:30 and I swam 30 minutes and I felt good. No stomach issues, and my swim pace each morning feels stronger than the previous day.

I had another breakfast after the swim and we relaxed by the hotel pool for a couple of hours. While we were sitting there, the pool attendant asked me for my autograph! I didn't know whether to feel complimented or embarrassed. Turns out she has kept an autograph book filled with hundreds of autographs from Ironman athletes over the years.

I ran again for about 30 minutes at midday, this time out on the Queen K. I keep trying to acclimate to the heat as much as possible. Boy, it's hot out there!! I must remember my bad experience last year when I tried to run the Queen K. Hydrate, hydrate, hydrate.

This afternoon, I organized my transition bags. to be dropped off tomorrow at registration. There are two bags - Transition 1 (swim to bike) which stays on the pier, and Transition 2 (bike to run) which will be transported down to the Kona Surf Hotel.*

I used my checklist and double checked everything, even the unusual. I packed an extra pair of contact lenses in the T 1 bag in case I lose a lens in the swim; sunscreen in both bags; an extra pair of dry socks for the run in case my feet get soaked on the bike from spilled water or sweat. I don't want to start the run with wet feet and get blisters early in the marathon.

After an early dinner, Dave and I went down to the Athletes' Parade starting point. Dave's Press Pass got him into the area restricted for athletes only and he got several good photos.

After the parade, I saw Dave Scott. He signed a 1994 Ironman poster which I know I'll hang on the wall in my den.

Tomorrow's a big and busy day. Early to bed again.

* In 1994, the bike course ended at the Kona Surf Hotel in Keauhou, six miles south of the Pier. After T2, athletes ran south on Alii Drive and into "The Pit" - a steep downhill section of road. At the bottom of the Pit was a turnaround, and then up the hill and north back to town. Several years later the course was changed and both T1 and T2 were re-located onto the Pier.

Wednesday, October 12th.

We were up early enough so that I started my swim at 7 am. I swam farther this morning than on any of my previous swims - past the Kings buoy and more than 2000 meters. Interesting that up until I got to the Kings buoy, visibility was clear down to the ocean bottom, even when we were in about 60 feet of water. Shortly after that, the depth dropped drastically and I could no longer see bottom. It was eerie at first, until I got used to it. I'm glad my first experience of that was in training and not on race day.

After breakfast, I put my aero race wheels on the bike, cleaned and lubed the chain, and rode about 15 miles. Everything is in good working order.... the wheels, the bike, and me!

After the bike ride I ran in and out of "The Pit". Two words came to mind. "HOT" and "STEEP". I'll be running that early in the marathon; between miles 2 and 4, so my legs will be as fresh as I can expect them to be that day. I'll be more than a mile off the bike so I should have my "running legs" and I won't be fatigued from running at the end of the marathon.

This afternoon also was the athletes' pre-race meeting. It went like most others. I found one remark form the race physician to be very curious. He said that despite rumors which were circulating in town, an IV is not automatically included in the race registration fee, and if an IV needs to be given to an athlete in the finish line medical tent, there will be a charge. I'm not sure if he was serious or trying to be funny.

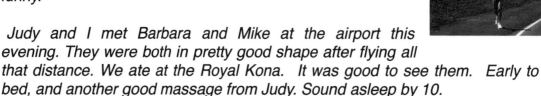

Judy and I met Barbara and Mike at the airport this evening. They were both in pretty good shape after flying all that distance. We ate at the Royal Kona. It was good to see them. Early to bed, and another good massage from Judy. Sound asleep by 10.

Thursday, October 13th.

I didn't sleep well last night. I'm starting to get the usual pre-race worries about all the ridiculous things that most probably won't go wrong, but, in my dreams, always go haywire. Race logistics, check-in, will I have enough time in the morning to set up my transition spot, etc. I hope I sleep better tomorrow night. I need the rest.

I swam at 7:30. The water was flat as a lake, and there's a noticeable difference in the tide. It's getting lower and there's much more beach than there was earlier in there week.

Judy and I spent some time working on my estimated pace and where on the course I might be at different times in the day. Her plan is to drive wherever she can on the course throughout the day. With all the running around she has planned, she's going to be as tired as I will be by the end of the day.

I rode briefly out on the Queen K. The wind was mild in both directions which is very unusual, but that means nothing for race day. Ironman veterans tell stories about how in earlier years, the wind was virtually non-existent on Friday and then horrendous on race day. You can't predict; you can only hope fore the best and prepare for the worst.

Tonight was the traditional carbo-loading party. It's held outside in a huge parking lot. behind the King Kam Hotel. There were big tents set up, a stage and band stand. There was good food and plenty of it. There were videos from previous years' races - '91, '92, and '93. NBC coverage of the last two races was awesome. The night ended early with music and fireworks.

Friday, October 14th.

I slept OK last night, although I did wake up a few times. Still had a few nutsy dreams about race day problems. Funny, but the problems I dream about are never about me performing good or bad. They are usually about a mechanical problem; leaky swim goggles; losing a running shoe in T2!

I woke up at 6:30 and, as planned, did not swim. In fact today will be a complete rest day for me.

After a big breakfast of waffles, I cleaned and lubed my bike one last time before bike inspection and check-in which is schedule at noon.

I was at bike check-in at 12:00 on the dot. The inspection was more thorough than I expected it to be, but without any problems for me. I guess it makes sense to do a complete inspection in advance rather than have a mechanical problem when you're 50 miles out on the Queen K. One suggestion that the bike inspector made which I would not have done, was to release some of the air pressure from my tires. If the tires are at full pressure and the bike sits in the hot afternoon sun for several hours, there's a good chance one or both of the tires will blow.

The actual bike check-in however was traumatic for us all. It's hard to describe the feeling when you give up your bike to be racked in the transition area. Everyone gets quiet and serious, checking over and over again the exact spot where their bike is placed. The next time I'll see my bike will be race morning. So close, after all these months of preparation. I'm glad I had the foresight to cover the aerobar shifters with plastic in case of rain. It poured rain all night long. One thing I didn't think to do - which I'll do next time, if there is a next time - is to bring some chain lubricant with me on race morning. The heavy rain washed away most of the silicone off my chain and it rubbed rough throughout the ride.

After a light pasta lunch, I went back to the room to elevate my feet and be alone with my thoughts. It was a good and restful three hours.

At 6 pm we all met for dinner at the Seafood Pasta Palace. There were eight of us. Barbara and Mike, other friends Ralph and Lorraine (who were on their honeymoon in Maui and came over for the race), Dave and his girlfriend Jean, Judy and me. I'm glad we made a reservation. Even though it was an early dinner, the restaurant was packed.

Dave got to the restaurant a little late because he had to attend a mandatory pre-race photographers' meeting. (More about that later. ...) I ate a plate of spaghetti marinara and several glasses of water. Good menu choice. There was a lot of good conversation , some laughs, and encouragement from everybody. Ralph kept kidding me about sharks. I probably wasn't very good

company that night. I was hearing all the chatter, but I was somewhat oblivious to everything around me; wrapped up in my own thoughts. Soon after dinner, Judy and I left the others so we could get an early start back to the hotel. It was still pouring rain. We went to bed about 9:30. Sleep came quickly, but it was intermittent, with thoughts about the rain, whether it would stop in time for the race, and about what was in store for me tomorrow.

Race Day. Saturday October 15th.

I didn't need the alarm to wake me at 3:45. I was up like a shot! Following my usual morning routine, I got down on the floor to stretch. Then I started to do my usual 100+ sit-ups when I stopped and said to Judy " This is dumb. I really don't need to do sit-ups this morning. I'm gonna get plenty of exercise today."

I ate a banana, a piece of bread and drank some Gatorade. (in hindsight, not nearly enough of a breakfast for an Ironman). I got dressed in my swim suit sandals and a T-shirt, and took one last inventory of my race gear. Everything was packed and ready from the night before. Two pair of goggles, swim cap, two water bottles with water and Gatorade, bike pump, sunglasses. Dave knocked on our door with his camera ready. I applied sunscreen, Vaseline where I needed it, and we were out the door at 4:30 am.

Since it was only a two-minute walk from the hotel to the Pier, I was the first athlete to arrive. The pier entrance was fenced and locked and a security guard told me that athletes weren't allowed onto the pier until 5 am. So I was set to wait. I think other athletes were watching out their hotel windows because within a couple of minutes dozens more started showing up. And now I can say that I was first in my inaugural Ironman … for check-in.

Everyone was nervous but spirits were high. A little before 5 am, the NBC army arrived. There were dozens of them with all sorts of equipment and cameras. They started taping the introduction remarks right where I was standing. They taped the same thing over and over again, seven or eight times, and every time I was in the line of the camera. (Months later, when we watched the NBC coverage of Ironman, there I was on TV. My 15 seconds of fame.)

5 am race morning. Waiting for the gates to open. The anxiety is palpable.

The pier gates finally opened at 5 o'clock. I got my body marked. #621. The volunteers were great. They helped us stay calm and relaxed. One volunteer helped me top off my tires with air, set up my water bottles and put my shoes into my bike cleats. My bike was ready and so was I, and it was only 5:15. Better early than late.

After I got everything set up, I felt more relaxed. The nervous pre-race anxiety left. The early planning, preparation and organization paid off.

I found Judy, Dave, Jean, Barbara and Mike near the beach, sitting on the sea wall. They managed to get a good viewing spot for the swim start. I had enough time to walk back to our room to drop off the extra gear, bike pump, etc. and when I got back to the sea wall about 6 am, Ralph and Lorraine had arrived. There was some small talk and good luck wishes. I think everyone was nervous, and I decided to say my good-byes and head over to the beach for a warm-up swim even though it was still a little early. Judy was very emotional when she hugged and kissed me. I remember tasting the salt from her tears as I walked away.

There weren't too many athletes in the water when I got there, so I decided it would be a good time to do my warm up strokes and find my spot for the start. The water was warm and flat. Beautiful. As I was treading water waiting for the starting gun, I was pleasantly surprised how relaxed and at peace I felt. I knew I had prepared and planned well for this day. Now all I had to do was stay in the moment and race my best.

I positioned myself behind the Body Glove Boat at the starting line and to the left of the pack and when the cannon sounded I had a clean start with virtually no body bumping. When I got out into the open water, the sea swells became more noticeable, and I was glad I could breathe on both sides. I timed my breaths when I was at the top of a swell to minimize the chances of swallowing water and also to help with navigation. It all worked well, but I was surprised that the time clock at the turn-around boat showed 45 minutes. That was a good five minutes slower than expected. The return leg of the swim must have had the benefit of the current because I came out of the water in one hour 20 minutes. Right on target.

I jogged through the fresh water showers (hanging hoses really), grabbed my T1 bag, and sprinted into the changing tent. There were volunteers inside the tent helping us get organized, changed in cycling shorts and ready for the bike. As I exited the tent about six minutes later I heard my race number being called. And as I got to where my bike had been racked, there was another volunteer with my bike out of the rack and ready for me to mount and go. Boy were they efficient!

Riding out off of the Pier was exhilarating. The crowds were yelling and screaming, and then I hit the first hill on Palani Road. "Pay 'n Save Hill" as it's called, is probably a little less than half a mile of climbing but it feels a lot longer. And since my legs weren't warmed up yet it felt all the more daunting. I was glad I had pre-set my gears in a low gear as I stated to climb the long steep hill up to the Queen K Highway.

Judy and the gang were waiting about half way up Palani Road which helped me power my way up to the top. But then as I turned left on the Queen K, I was enveloped in the absolute sound of silence. There are very few spectators out on the Queen K so it's very quiet. All you hear is the sound of the chain spinning, the tires against the road surface and your own breathing. And so I settled in to what would be more than seven hours of riding, mostly in complete silence.

There were several good breaks in the silence though. When I approached Waikoloa (about mile 15), Judy and the gang were there yelling and howling support as planned. Again in Hawi at the bike turn-around (mile 50) they were all there. I reached Hawi in under four hours, as expected. My average speed was about 17 mph. Good. The return trip on the bike however was a lot harder for me. By that point in the bike, the cyclists are much more spread out and while you can see other riders in front of you and behind you, for all intents and purposes, you are riding alone. In addition to fatigue, the heat and wind started to take their toll on my body. The heat of the sun across my shoulders made me feel like a steak on a BBQ, and the hot winds seemed to blow in my face no matter which direction I was going. Once or twice I thought about stopping for a brief moment's rest, but there was no shade anywhere, and stopping would not help me get to the finish line. I adjusted my gears. My speed slowed but I kept spinning.

And then I saw the "mirage". I was at about mile 75, alone on the Queen K. A far distance away on the left shoulder of the road, I saw something standing there. I couldn't see clearly what it was. It had that wavy appearance drivers see on road surfaces on blazing hot days. At first I thought it one of the famous wild donkeys that live out on the lava fields. But as I got closer I saw that it was a person. And as I got closer still, I realized it was my son Dave. Alone in the heat waiting for me, his camera ready. As I went by, he took a burst of photos; I could hear the camera clicks. Then a little while later, a small flat bed truck came up on my side, and there was Dave again in the back of the flat bed riding next to me and taking pictures. His press pass had gotten him complete access on the Queen K, and he managed to get a ride out and back just so he could capture that moment on film. It was very uplifting to see him there at that moment. I'm sure it helped me push on for many miles.

After seven and half hours, I pulled into the Kona Surf Hotel and T2. As in T1 after the swim, the volunteers were more than helpful. They had my T2 run gear bag ready for me as I entered the changing tent, and they gave me help changing into my running gear and applied sunscreen across my burning shoulders. I was glad I had packed a dry pair of socks. The pair I wore on the bike were soaked through with sweat, water and Gatorade. Starting the marathon in those drenched socks would have spelled pain for the run.

And so about 4 pm, with the sun still burning hot, I ran out of T2 and started the 26.2 mile run.

You may find this hard to believe, but it actually felt good to be starting the marathon. Both physically (I was off that damned bike saddle) and emotionally (I had so much completed behind me and I was getting closer to the finish line), I felt pretty good.

As I expected, my thighs were tight at the start of the run. My plan was not to push the pace at the start. I went easy and shortened my stride, figuring it would take five minutes or more before my legs "opened up". As it turned out, going slow and keeping my stride short wasn't an option. Within a quarter mile of exiting T2, I was faced with a very steep climb out of the hotel parking lot up *to Alii Drive. And then after about another half mile on Alii Drive, the course went down into The Pit to the ocean, and back up another very steep climb. Two very steep hills and I hadn't gone two miles yet!*

The next six miles were all on Alii Drive, a quiet tree covered road that parallels the water. It was very scenic, but also very hot and humid. Thankfully the road was lined with a lot of cheering, encouraging spectators. At about mile 9, we ran back through the town of Kailua Kona, past the Pier, and back up Palani Road. It was no more fun running up Palani Road, than it had been cycling up many hours earlier. Judy and the gang were there again, encouraging me up the hill and out of town, back onto the Queen K.

There were aid stations positioned every mile on the run. They offered water, Gatorade, bananas, orange slices and ice cold sponges to help cool down. We also were offered a new Gatorade carbohydrate gel. It was a novelty then, and a brilliant way to replace calories without upsetting your stomach. I walked through each station, partially to rest and also so I could eat and drink without splashing my feet. Dry feet meant less chance of blisters forming. As the sun started to get lower in the sky, I was approaching the half way point in the marathon. I ran down into the Natural Energy Lab - two miles in and two miles out, and when I got back onto the Queen K, I estimated that I had only about 15 K (9+ miles) remaining to the finish line. Even though my confidence was building that I was going to finish the race, my pace slowed even more. I was walking a lot more than I wanted, but I figured "run / walk / run" was better than "DNF".

In the 1980's and early 1990's there were no street lights on the Queen K. And since the highway ran next to the black lava fields, everything was completely dark. For safety reasons, the runners are given phosphorescent glow sticks so they are visible.

Now, after dark, the road was completely covered in darkness. Looking down the highway, all you could see were green phosphorescent semi circles bouncing their way along the shoulder of there road. The only time we had some light was at the aid stations where they used generators to give the volunteers enough light so they could see what they were doing. And the darkness also brought a change to the menu selections at the aid stations. In addition to the usual water and Gatorade, we now had a choice of warm chicken stock and saltine crackers to replace the depleted salt in out bodies.

I was approaching town again at about mile 24. Barely running up the last incline before the down turn to Palani Road, and I heard my name being called on the sound system. In my oxygen deprived confusion, I thought it was the finish line announcer and I started to pick up my pace. Quickly however I realized it was the last aid station and they were calling out the runners names to encourage them over that last hill and into town. But there were still about two miles to go.

I was now on automatic pilot. I ran down Hualalai Road, made a right turn onto Alii Drive and started my run towards the finish line chute about a quarter mile away. There's a dog leg turn to the left on Alii Drive at that point, and as I made the slight turn I was enveloped in the light and cheers of the fans as I ran through the chute to the final finish. I crossed the finish and heard "Frank Adornato, You Are An Ironman".

It was almost 10 pm when I finished. 14 hours and 54 minutes since I started the swim at 7 am. There at the finish line was Judy. A big hug, a lei around my neck and tears of joy. Dave was close behind Judy and with a smile almost as big as mine.

After collecting my medal and taking finishers photos we met up with the rest of the gang. I took a well appreciated shower and we all had a late celebration dinner, looking down at the finish line as other triathletes ran, walked and limped their way to becoming an Ironman. During dinner, Dave reminded me about his arriving late for dinner on Friday evening. As he had told me, he was at a press meeting. What he didn't tell me then was that there was a lot of discussion about the weather forecast, and the winds were expected to be much stronger than in previous years. They were right, and I'm glad I didn't know that before hand.

We stayed until midnight when the last finisher came in, and then it was straight to bed for a sound deep sleep. I honestly don't remember if I dreamed at all that night; I was too exhausted. But if I did dream I'm sure I was in a happy place.

Some post-notes:

After this first Ironman in 1994, I went on to race four more Ironman events. Hawaii 1997, where I shaved almost an hour off my finish time; Ironman Lake Placid 1999, and Ironman Florida 2000 and 2002. Each race was faster than the previous, and my best finish was 12 hour 36 minutes in 2002.

Judy and I loved going to Kona, and eventually we purchased a small condo and Kona became our second home for about ten years.

In 1995, I earned a College Certification as a Fitness Specialist. As I got ready for my retirement from corporate America, I starting coaching endurance athletes - mostly triathletes and marathon runners. Over the years I expanded my client base to include wellness training as well as competitive coaching. I'm still coaching and loving it.

As of this writing, I continue to train and race, mostly Sprint and Olympic distance triathlons, as well as running races up to the half marathon. My fitness level and competitive edge has stayed strong, and I often finish at or near the top of my age group. May 2015 will mark my thirtieth anniversary as a triathlete.

For more information on my coaching services, please visit my website at www.triitall.com.

Train smart. Race fast.

Frank Adornato

Race Day

A lot of emotion as I get ready for my warm up swim.   Into the water and ready for the cannon to fire.

The swim start.

Out of the water and on my way to the transition tent.

Somewhere on the Queen K. Dave took this photo while sitting on the flat bed back of a pick up truck.

The silence and magnitude of the Queen K.

Walking through an aid station. Gatorade, and a cold sponge.

Trying some of the new Carbo gel.

Printed in Great Britain
by Amazon